CREATIVE COLORING FOR GROWN-UPS

TATTOO DESIGNS

METRO BOOKS

New York

METRO BOOKS
New York

An Imprint of Sterling Publishing
1166 Avenue of the Americas
New York, NY 10036

METRO BOOKS and the distinctive Metro Books logo are trademarks of
Sterling Publishing Co., Inc.

© 2014 by Michael O'Mara Books

Designed by Billy Waqar
Cover by Claire Cater

Illustrations by Iván Cruz, Matteo Buscicchio, Erik Batista,
Ezster David, Maz SpiralOut Art, Ale Abuelita, Greg Stevenson,
Pachu Garcia and Shutterstock.com

ISBN 978-1-4351-5881-8

For information about custom editions, special sales, and premium and
corporate purchases, please contact Sterling Special Sales at 800-805-5489 or
specialsales@sterlingpublishing.com.

Manufactured in Canada

4 6 8 10 9 7 5 3

www.sterlingpublishing.com

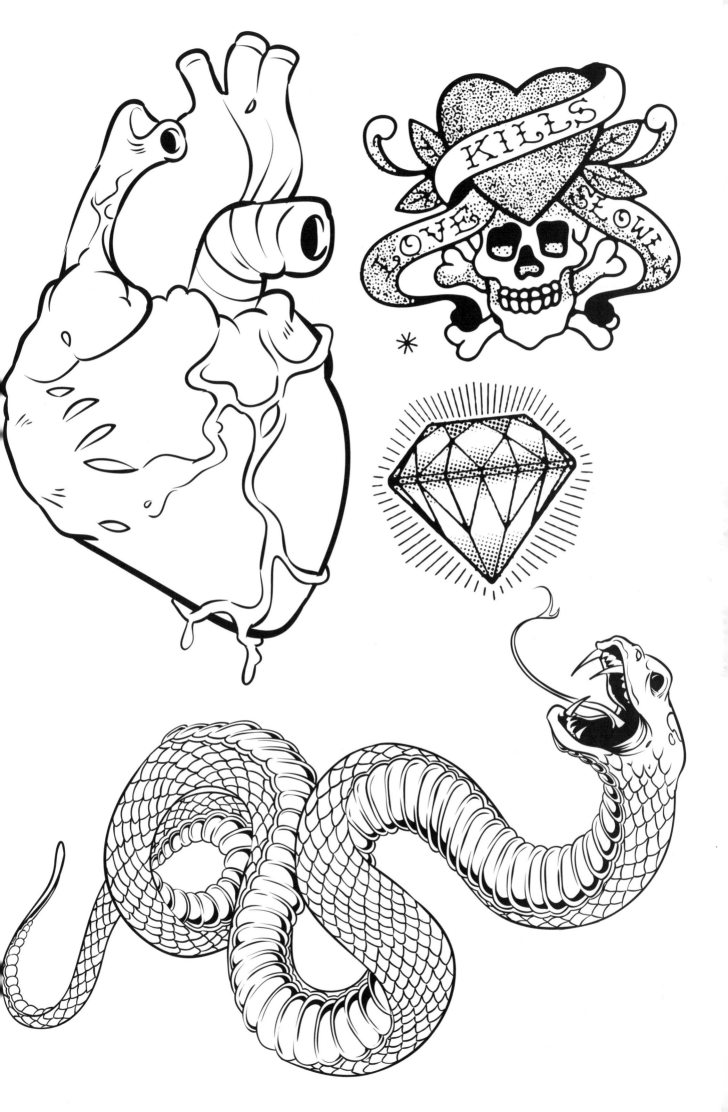

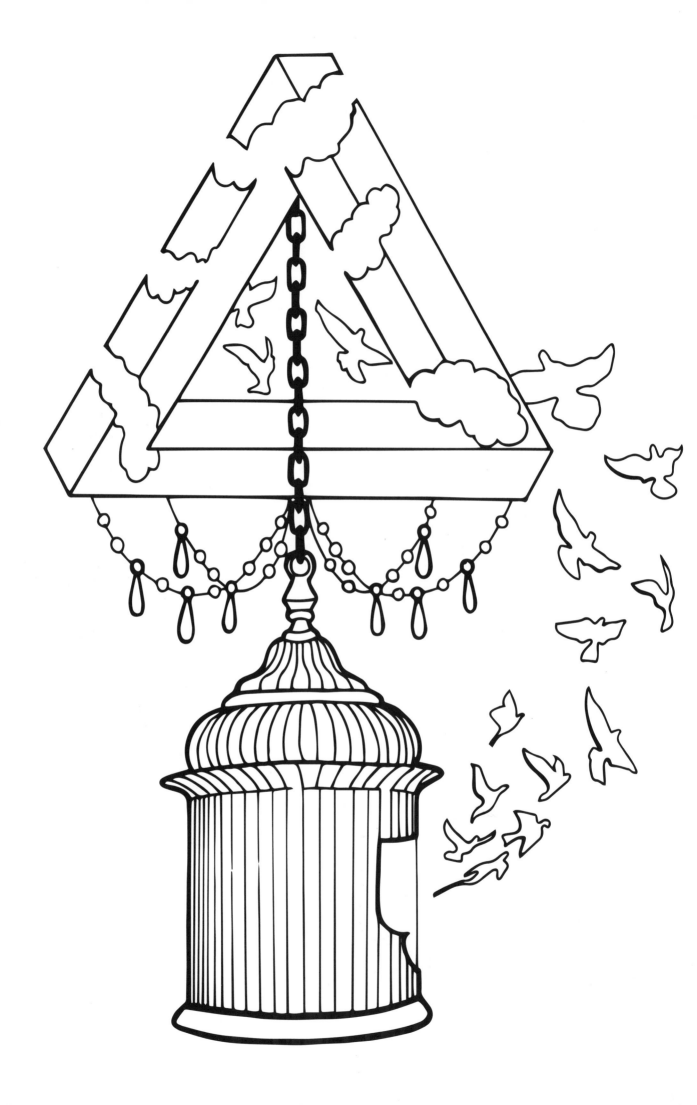

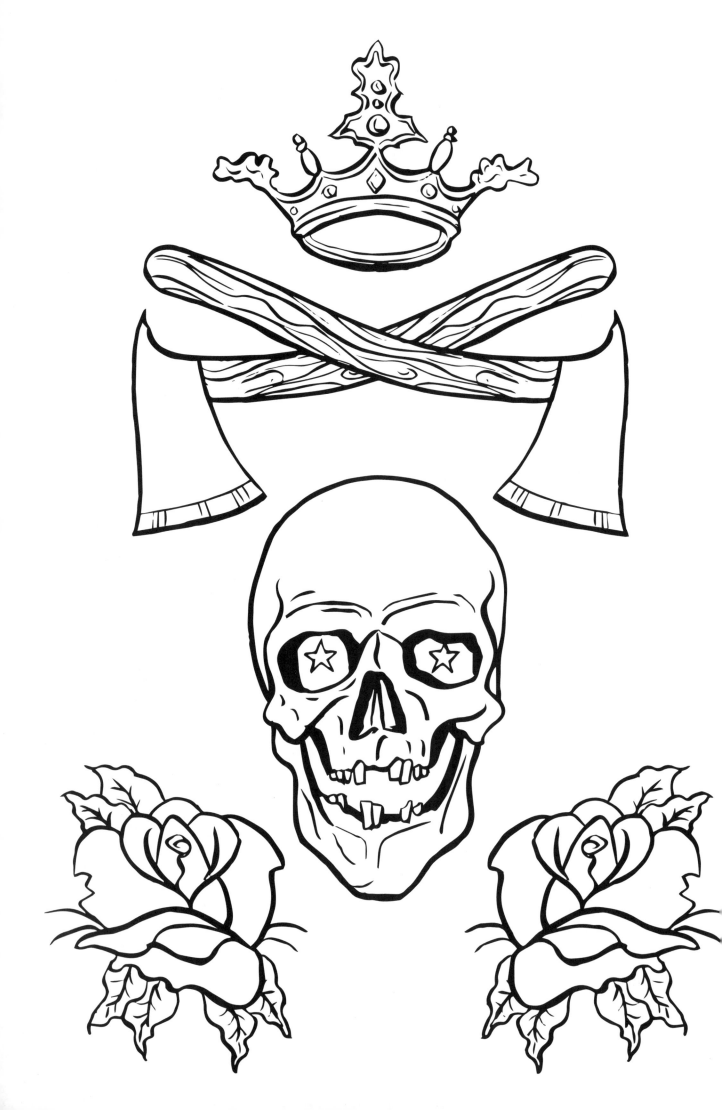

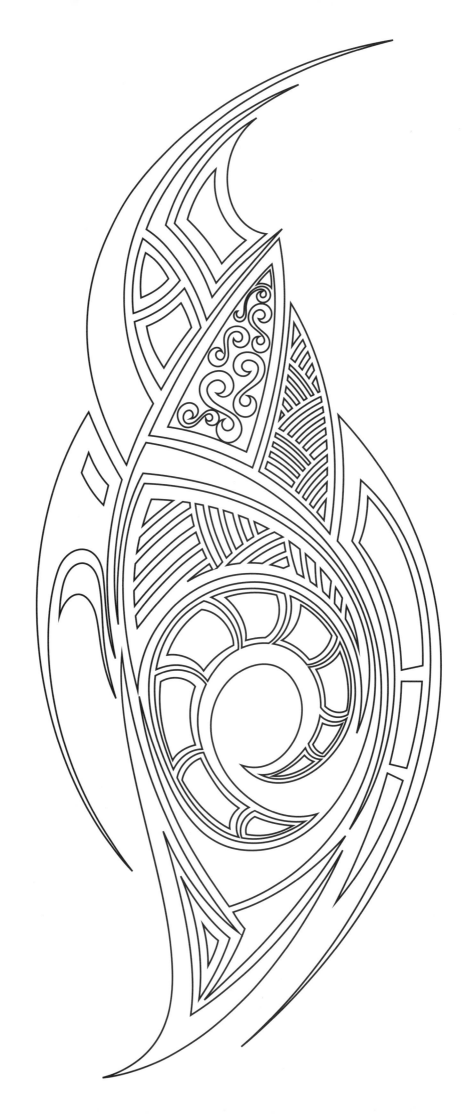

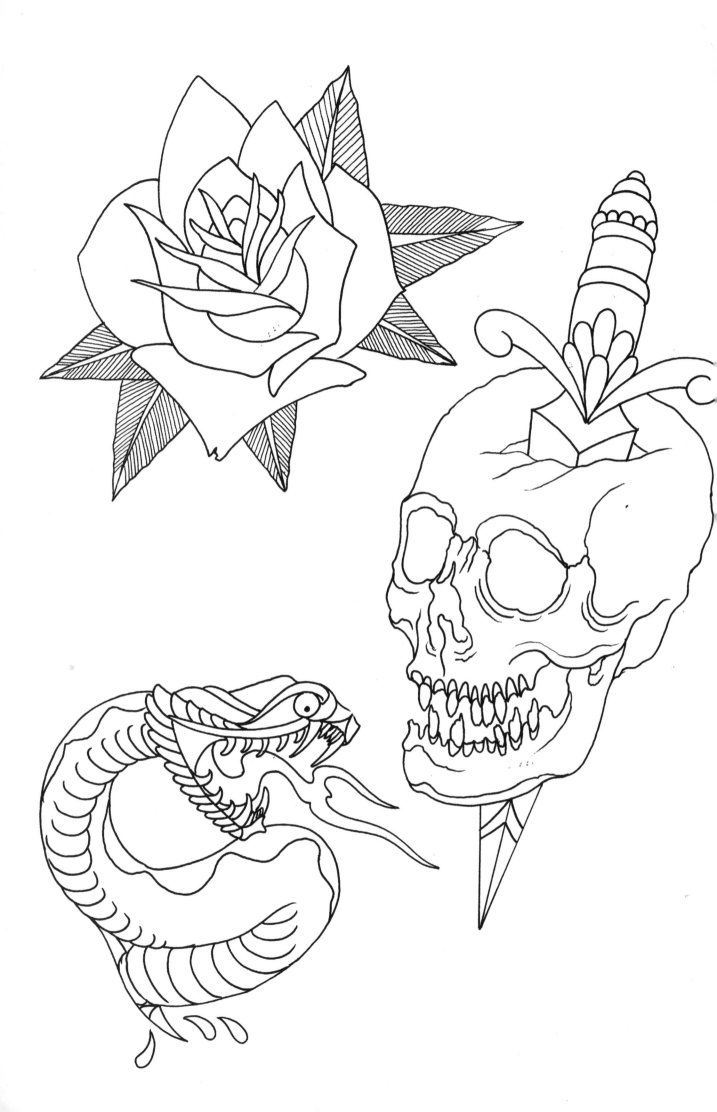

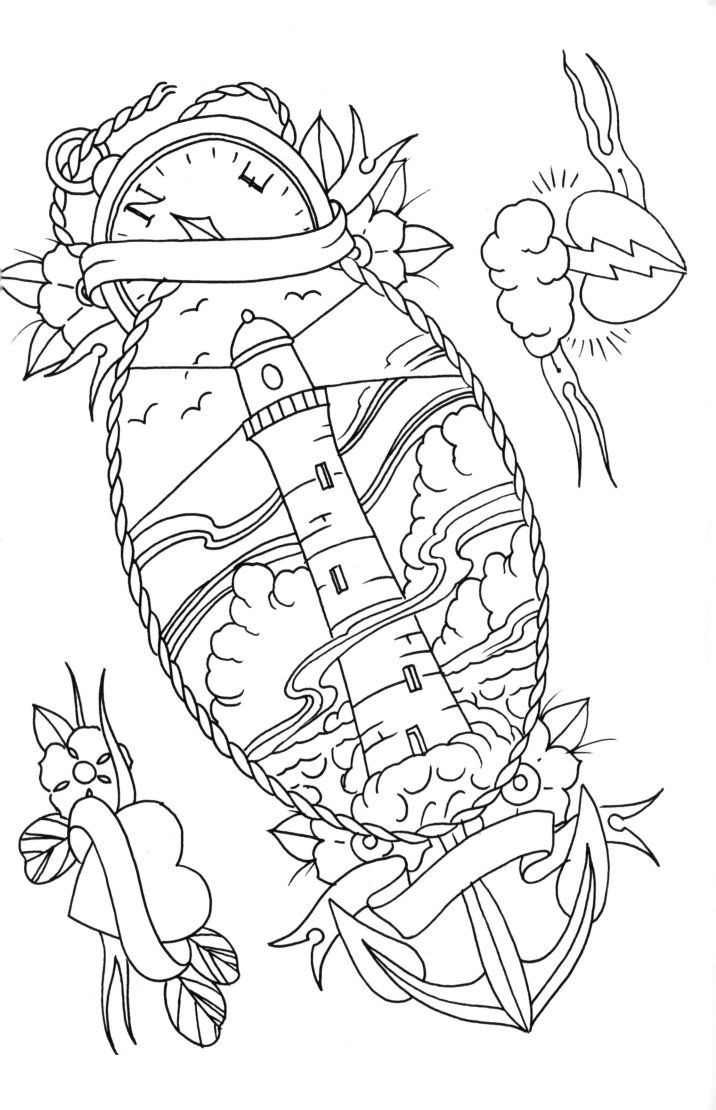

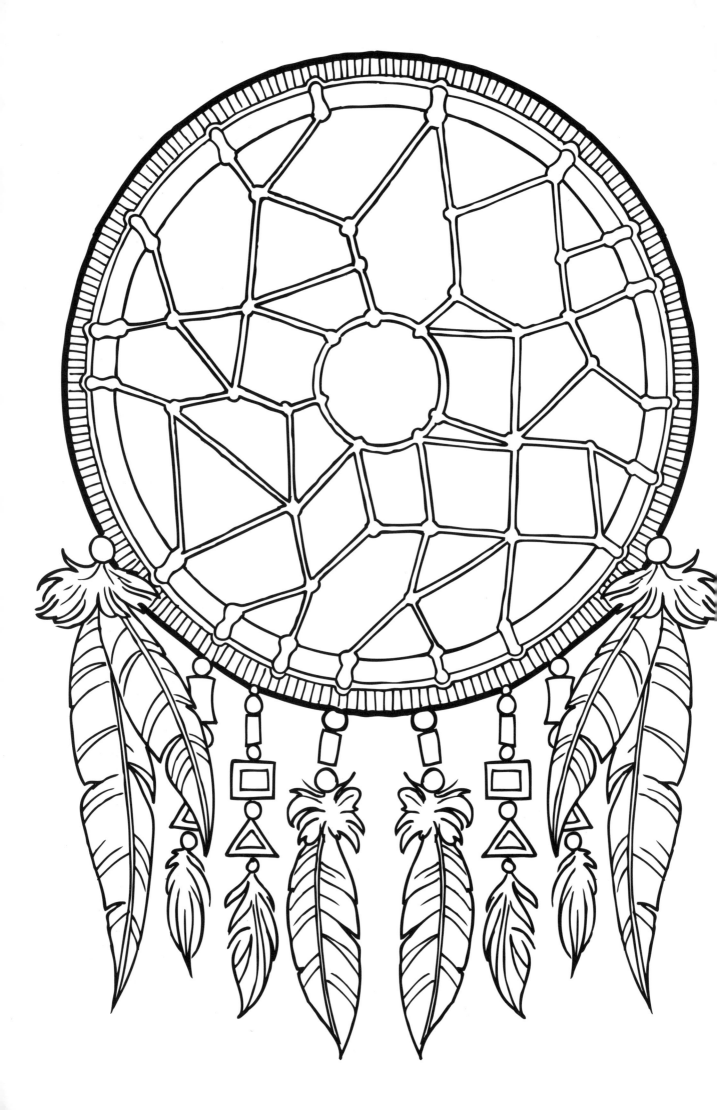